Tina Finds a Way

written by Geof Smith
illustrated by June Goldsborough

McGraw-Hill
School Division

New York   Farmington

I. THE PLAY

The play was only a week away. All the girls and boys in Mrs. Brown's class were excited, but Tina Lau was the most excited of all. She was going to be Little Red Riding Hood, and her family was coming to see her.

"Please line up," Mrs. Brown said. "I'm handing out the tickets for Saturday's play." Tina glanced at her ticket. "But Mrs. Brown, there are only two tickets here."

"That's right, Tina. Each child in class gets two."

"But two isn't enough," Tina said. "I need four."

Mrs. Brown said, "I'm sorry. There just isn't enough space to include all our friends and family. You'll have to decide whom to ask."

After school, Tina walked slowly to her house. The clouds above were dark. When she turned the corner, a wild wind blew her hat off and into a puddle. The whole world looked bad. She had worked hard to learn her lines, repeated them over and over and learned to say them so everyone would understand the story of the play. Everybody told her she was great. Now her whole family wouldn't even see her. Who would get to go and who wouldn't?

2. THE PROBLEM

At home, Tina sat at the table, her head down. "What's wrong?" Tina's brother, Brian, asked. Tina explained her problem.

"That is a problem," Brian said. "But I don't have to go. I can stay home and watch the ball game on television."

Even if Brian didn't go, Tina was only half
way to an answer. She had three more
people to ask, but only two tickets. One other
person would not be able to go.

Tina talked to her mother, who was reading the newspaper. "I would love to see you in the play," Tina's mother said, "but I'd certainly understand if you took your father and grandmother."

When Tina asked her father, he said that she should take her mother and grandmother. "I don't want to miss your special day, but I might have to work next Saturday."

Tina put on her coat and crossed the street to Grandmother Lau's house. "Take your mother and father, Tina. You can come over after the play for juice and cookies and tell me all about it."

Tina's whole family understood that she could only get two tickets. Her mother, father, grandmother, and brother each wanted to help her by not coming to see the play. But Tina wanted them all to be there.

3. THE ANSWER

The next morning at school, Tina ran to find Mrs. Brown. "The lunchroom," Tina said. "We can do the play in there!"

"Well, that is an idea, Tina. It's a bigger room. It's not exactly set up to put on a play. But let's see what we can do."

Later on, Mrs. Brown took Tina aside in the lunchroom. "It's all set," she told Tina. "Now all the children can bring their entire families. We'll tell them tomorrow. Thanks for your good idea!"

That Saturday afternoon, all the Laus
went to school. A painted moon hung on one
wall. A tall candle sat on a desk. The front of
the lunchroom looked like an old house.

Tina stood behind a sheet and peeked
out. She was very excited. What if something
went wrong? What if she forgot what to say?

Nothing went wrong. Tina was a great
Little Red Riding Hood. She was the star of
the play, but everybody else was good, too.
Mrs. Brown was happy. And all four of Tina's
guests were very proud!